WONDERFUL ME!

10 Songs for young children involving them
in body awareness and use of their senses.

2 to 7 years

Written and illustrated by

CAROLINE HOILE

Edited by ALISON HEDGER

SONGS

1   My Body
2   Bones and Muscles
3   Skin
4   My Legs
5   My Head and Face
6   I Can Touch
7   I Can Smell
8   I Can Hear
9   I Can Taste
10   I Can See

A selection of new "get up and join in" songs, together with songs based on sensory perception. Ideas are given for numbers 6 to 10, to help teachers utilise the full potential of each song.

Ten uncomplicated and happy melodies with simple piano accompaniment and guitar chords.

A tape of the songs for use where no pianist is available is played and sung by Alison Hedger and is obtainable from the Publishers.

© Copyright 1991 Golden Apple Productions
A division of Chester Music Limited
8/9 Frith Street, London W1V 5TZ

ISBN I 870997 31 X
Order No: GA10450

1.
MY BODY

Repeat the music between each verse for the actions

2.   I can make my body bend

3.   I can make my body twist

4.   I can make my body curl

5.   I can make my body turn

6.   I can make my body spiky

7.   I can make my body floppy

2.
BONES AND MUSCLES

Play an octave higher for a skeleton dance

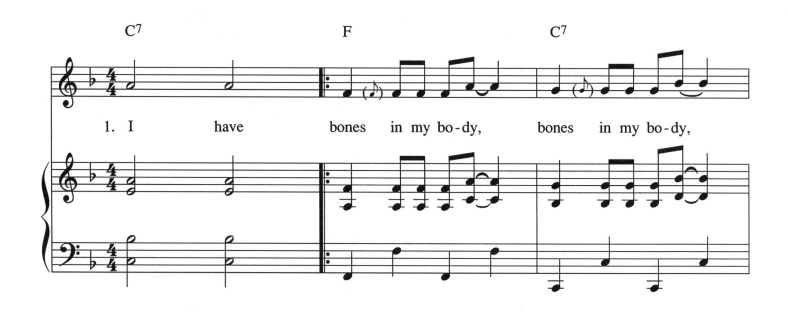

1. I have bones in my bo-dy, bones in my bo-dy,

First time — Second time

bones in my bo-dy I have. I have keep-ing me in shape.

2. I have muscles in my body,
       muscles in my body,
   Muscles in my body I have.
   I have muscles in my body,
       muscles in my body
   Making me so strong!

How about tubes, lungs and heart?
The exact wording of these verses will be left to your imagination.
Best avoided with the very young!!

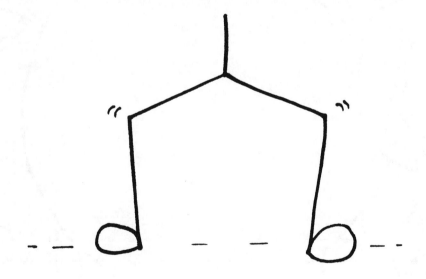

3.
SKIN

I've got skin to keep me all in!

I've got skin you know! I've got skin to

keep me all in. It stre - tches as I grow!

4.
MY LEGS

Make the accompaniment echo the actions.

(e.g. for "HOP" leave out the smaller notes in the L.H.)

2. My legs can hop

3. My legs can skip

4. My legs can bend

5. My legs can stamp

6. My legs can march

7. My legs can kick

8. My legs can slide

9. My legs can swing

10. My legs can .... JUMP

5.
MY HEAD and FACE

I have a head on my neck. I have a head on my neck. I have a head on my neck, and I can nod with it.

2. I have some hair on my head, which keeps my head quite warm!

3. I have some brains in my head, and I can think with them.

4. I have two ears on my head, and I can hear with them.

5. I have a tongue in my head, and I can talk (taste, click) with it.

6. I have a face in my head, and I express with it.

7. I have two eyes in my face, and I can see (blink, wink) with them.

8. I have a nose in my face, and I can smell (sneeze, sniff) with it.

9. I have a mouth in my face, and I can smile (talk, eat, kiss) with it.

10. I have some teeth in my mouth, and I can chew (bite, gnaw) with them.

6.
I CAN TOUCH

Repeat the music between each verse for the actions

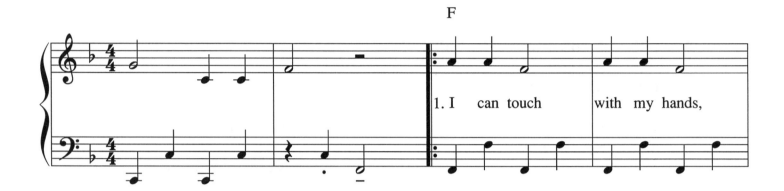

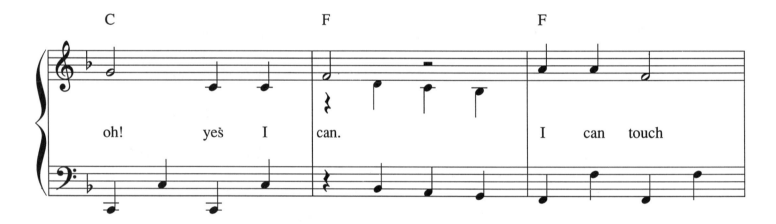

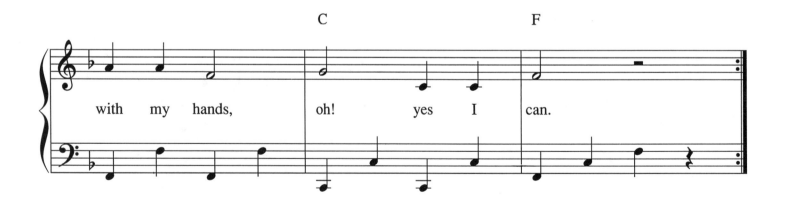

2. I can clap

3. I can tap

4. I can stroke

5. I can pat

6. I can click

7. I can knock

8. I can flick

9. I can shake

10. I can wave

Anything else...............?

Have several boxes with a front hole for hands to get inside but too small to see through. Place inside the boxes things which the children must identify by touch only. Concentrate on shapes with the very young e.g. (ball, box, brick, doll etc.) but experiment with the different feel of substances with older children e.g. (dry, granular, powdery, rough, smooth, furry, sticky etc.), See too whether they can identify materials by feel only e.g. (plastic, wood, nylon, cotton, metal, etc.).

7.
I CAN SMELL

A guess the smell song. Have ready a small sample of things with
distinctive smells - (polish, mint, onion, perfume, orange peel, sweets, etc...)
- in containers where the samples cannot be seen but the smell can escape.
Try a different smell before beginning the song each time.

Alternatively encourage the children to use their imaginations, and
conjure up the memory of distinctive smells.

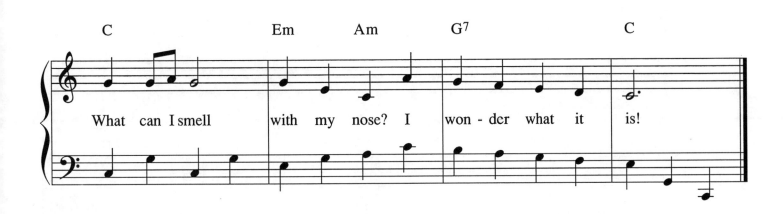

8.
I CAN HEAR

Have hidden from view things which make different sounds. See if the children can guess what they are and also see if they would class the sounds as loud, soft, high or low. See too whether they can tell from the sound what material the objects are made from eg. wood, plastic, metal etc.

2. With my ears I can hear lots of different sounds. (repeat)
SOFT SOUNDS, LOUD SOUNDS
Lots of in between sounds.
With my ears I can hear lots of different sounds.

9.
I CAN TASTE

Have ready samples of various foods, seasonings and spices.
Ask the children to taste each one and not only say what it is, but also if it is
sweet, sour, nice, nasty, bitter etc.... Be sure to warn them to only taste the
merest crumb or grain, just in case it is horrible. Obviously the younger the
children, the simpler the foods to be tested.

I use my tongue to taste all my food,
taste all my food, taste all my food. I use my tongue to
taste all my food. What can I taste now?

Child has a taste and says whether the taste is
sweet
bitter
sour
fruity
spicy or tingly

Continue with the second half of the song......

Alter the expression in Oh! to suit the taste - nice or nasty.

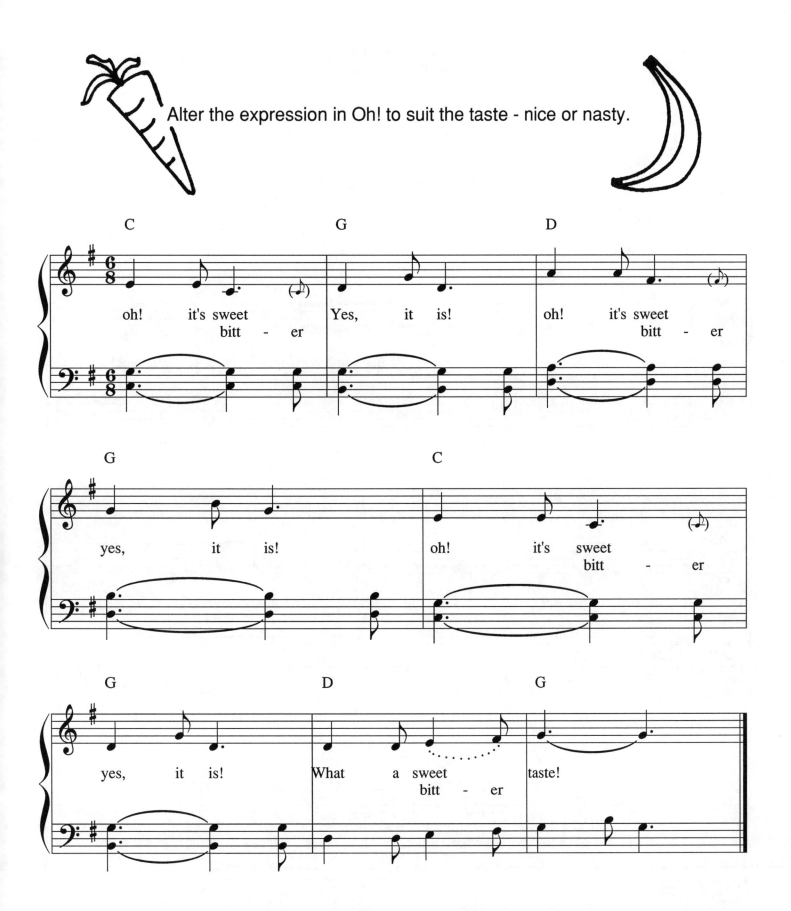

Change over the taster or the taste, and go back to the beginning of the song.

10.
I CAN SEE

Have various distinctively shaped objects - (soft toy, book, drum,
saucepan, bottle etc....) - hidden under a cloth. Reveal each object
in turn after singing and guessing.

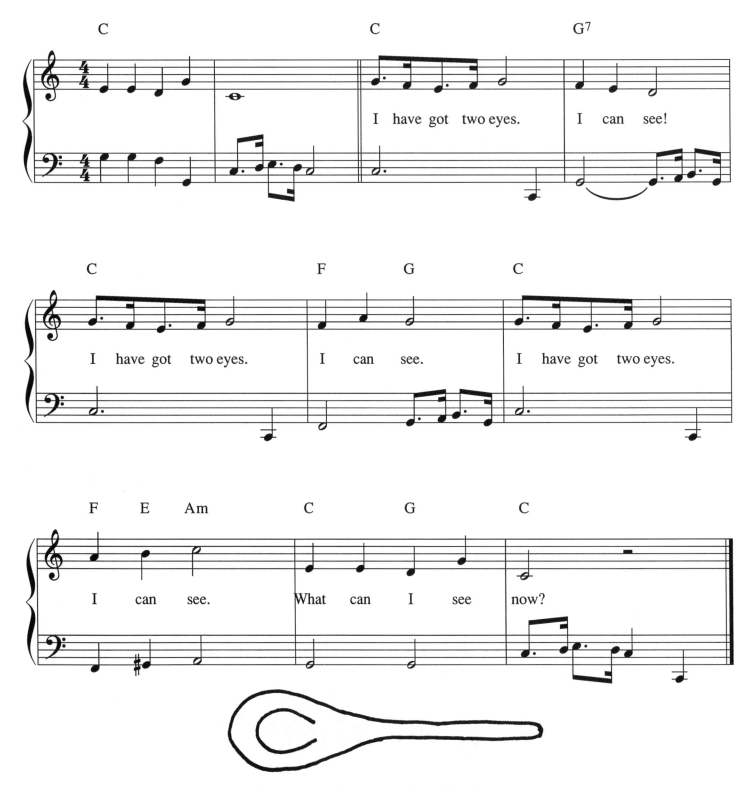

2/96 (23572)